CLOCK REPAIR

A Beginner's Guide

Ian Beilby

Clocks Magazine Beginner's Guide Series № 1

Published by Splat Publishing Ltd
141b Lower Granton Road
Edinburgh
EH5 1EX
United Kingdom

www.clocksmagazine.com

© 2008 Ian Beilby
World copyright reserved
Reprinted 2010, 2016

ISBN: 978 0 9562732 1 5

The right of Ian Beilby to be identified as author of this work has been asserted in accordance with the Copyright, Designs and Patents Act 1988. All rights reserved. No part of this publication may be reproduced, stored in a retrieval system, or transmitted in any form or by any means electronic, mechanical, photocopying, recording or otherwise, without the prior permission of the publisher.

4 6 8 10 9 7 5 3

Printed by Stephens & George, Goat Mill Road, Dowlais, Merthyr Tydfil CF48 3TD

CONTENTS

CLOCKS MAGAZINE BEGINNER'S GUIDE SERIES

No 1. Clock Repair, A Beginner's Guide
No 2. A Beginner's Guide to Pocket Watches
No 3. American Clocks, an Introduction
No 4: What's it Worth: A Price Guide to Clocks

IN PREPARATION

No 5. Make Your Own Clock, A Beginner's Guide

CHAPTER 1
THE MOVEMENT

Figure 1 shows a simple time-only—
or 'timepiece'—clock: it does not
'strike' the hours or 'chime' on the
quarters. You can see in **figure 2** I have
removed the mechanism or 'movement'
from the case, and in **figures 3** and **5**
I have made detailed annotated line

Figure 1.

drawings depicting the movement. From
figures 2 and **3** you will see that the
movement consists of a series of gears that
engage with each other. The large brass
'wheels' engage with the smaller steel
'pinions'. Both wheels and pinions run on
'arbors', not axles!

The steel pinions are cut integral with
the arbor. Each end of the arbor is turned

down or reduced slightly in order to
produce 'pivots'. The pivots run in 'pivot
holes' provided in the movement 'plates'.

The combined wheelwork is known
as a 'train' of wheels and is contained
between the front and back plate of the
movement. Four movement 'pillars'—one
at each corner—separate the two plates.
The pillars are usually permanently fixed
to the back plate (the plate furthest from
the hands). The front plate is attached to
the pillars with taper pins. Tapered spigots
are turned on the ends of the pillars, which
protrude through holes provided in the
front plate. The spigots are cross-drilled to
accept the taper pins.

On this movement the driving force for
the clock is provided by a powerful spring,
the 'mainspring', which is contained in
brass 'barrel' or 'going barrel'. The barrel
also acts as the driving wheel for the
movement via teeth cut into its periphery

Figure 3 shows the going barrel in
relation to the other wheels, it is not only
the largest, but also the first in the train of
wheels. The 'winding arbor'—the arbor on
which the going barrel runs—is provided
with a square on to which the clock key
fits. The inner coils of the spring are
attached to a 'hook' on the winding arbor,
and the outer coils are attached to a hook
in the wall of the barrel.

On the outside of the front plate a
ratchet wheel is fitted on to the square of
the winding arbor and a sprung 'click'
provided to keep the ratchet wheel in
place. The ratchet wheel and click allow
the arbor to turn in a clockwise direction
only, retaining the power of the mainspring
and preventing the spring from unwinding
in the barrel.

Figure 2.

Once wound up the going barrel transfers its power through the intermediate wheel and the other wheels and pinions of the train until it reaches the final wheel in the train, the escape wheel.

An important arrangement of the gears on most domestic clocks is such that the centre wheel is designed to revolve clockwise once every hour. In **figures 3** and **5** you can see the centre wheel arbor is longer than the others and protrudes through the front plate of the movement. When the clock is assembled this arbor will protrude through the centre of the face or 'dial' and the minute hand will be affixed to it.

The centre arbor drives the 'motionwork' the name given to another set of gears, mounted on the front plate, that drives both hands in a clockwise direction. You can see the motionwork on this clock in **figure 4** as well as the winding square, ratchet wheel and click. For clarity, a drawing of just the motionwork and centre wheel is given in **figure 5**.

With this movement the motionwork comprises four gears. A small pinion of 16 teeth is attached to a 'pipe' made to be a tight fit on the centre arbor. This component is called the 'cannon pinion'. The end of the pipe

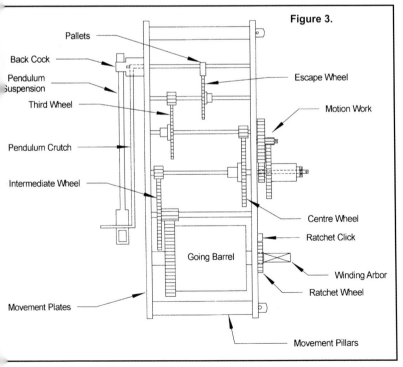

Figure 3.

Pallets
Back Cock
Pendulum Suspension
Third Wheel
Pendulum Crutch
Intermediate Wheel
Movement Plates

Escape Wheel
Motion Work
Centre Wheel
Ratchet Click
Going Barrel
Winding Arbor
Ratchet Wheel
Movement Pillars

is squared. The minute hand locates on this square. Running on the pipe of the cannon pinion is the hour wheel, which is also fitted with a pipe. The hour hand is fitted on to this pipe. Both the cannon pinion and hour wheels engage with another separate combined wheel and pinion fitted to the front plate. This wheel and pinion is usually called the minute wheel. The combined gearing of these wheels ensures that both hands turn in the same direction and provides a reduction of 12 to 1, ensuring that the hour hand turns only once for every 12 revolutions of the minute hand, *ie* once in every 12 hours

The speed of the hands is determined by the rate at which the centre hand is allowed to revolve. This is controlled at the top end of the gear train (the end furthest from the going barrel) by the rate at which the teeth of the 'escape wheel' are allowed pass through the 'pallets' of the 'escapement'.

Figure 4.

The escape wheel is so called because it allows the power of the clock to literally escape, in a controlled and regular manner. **Figure 6** is a drawing of a typical escape wheel and pallets. The teeth of the escape wheel are cut differently to conventional wheel teeth and the escapement is designed so that the escape wheel teeth are released one at a time by the pallets. At the same time as

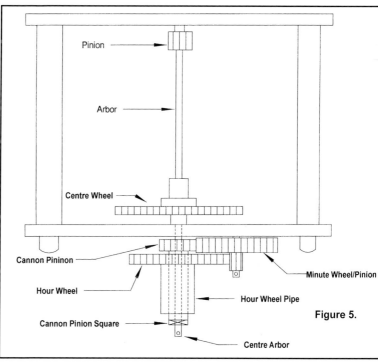

Figure 5.

9

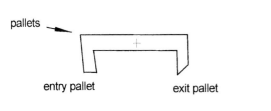

pallets

entry pallet   exit pallet

Figure 6.

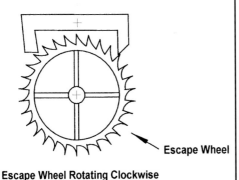

Escape Wheel

Escape Wheel Rotating Clockwise

length, thus governs the rate at which the escape wheel is allowed to turn and thus the rate at which the hands turn.

A photograph of the escape wheel and pallets is shown in **figure 7**.

You can see the pallets are attached to an arbor 'the pallet arbor' which protrudes through a hole in the back plate. The pendulum crutch is also attached to the pallet arbor. The arbor pivots in a separate bracket known as the 'back cock'. The back cock is attached to the back plate with two screws.

A length of spring steel known as the 'pendulum suspension' is also suspended from the back cock. The pendulum suspension fits through a slot provided in the pendulum crutch. The pendulum is then simply hooked on to the pendulum suspension.

The pendulum 'bob' can be moved slightly higher or lower on its rod by

Figure 7.

the escape wheel teeth engage the pallets they provide a little power, or 'impulse', to the pallets, which keeps the pendulum swinging. The rate at which the pendulum swings, which depends on its effective

turning a knurled nut below it, increasing or decreasing the frequency of swing of the pendulum respectively. Raising the bob speeds up the clock, and conversely lowering the bob slows the clock down.

CHAPTER 2
TOOLS & MATERIALS

Before dismantling and cleaning the movement we take a look at some of the simple hand tools and materials required when carrying out the dismantling and cleaning process. Where possible always buy good quality tools and progressively smaller ones when working on the movement itself.

A good range of sizes is vital. It is most important that the correct size of screwdriver is used if the screwdriver/screw head is not to be damaged. Never

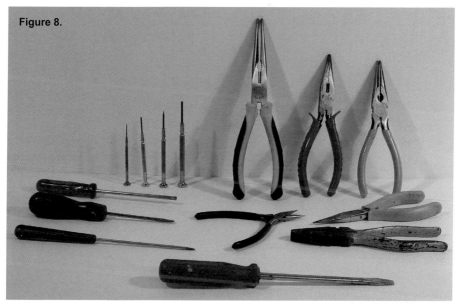

Figure 8.

made by a reputable manufacturer; in the long run they work out to be the cheapest by far.

Figure 8 illustrates a variety of screwdrivers and pliers, all of which are relatively inexpensive and easily obtained.

You can see various sizes of screwdriver are shown ranging from the small watchmaker's type up to the 1/4in domestic screwdriver. Larger screwdrivers are invariably needed when removing the movement from the case,

be tempted to use an approximate size of screwdriver. Always keep a firm grip on the handle and ensure that the screwdriver is located positively in the slot of the screw head.

Again, various sizes and types of pliers are required. Depending on the task in hand the most frequently used are flat pliers and round or nose-ended pliers. Pliers with serrated jaws offer greater grip especially when removing tapered clock pins, but they do have to be used with caution as they can easily mar the

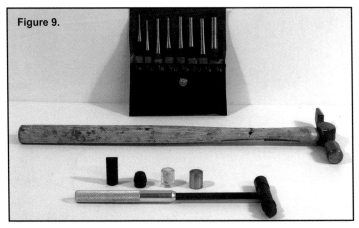

Figure 9.

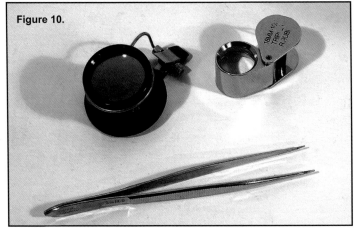

Figure 10.

surface of both brass and steel.

When using pliers for whatever purpose the secret is to ensure that not only the jaws of the pliers grip the component positively and firmly, but also the object is securely held as well.

A set of steel punches of differing diameters can be very useful. Quite often you find that short taper pins are difficult to grip and remove, and have to be coaxed free or punched out. In this connection a small hammer is also necessary. One of the hammers shown in **figure 9** is provided with interchangeable heads, making it suitable for many different applications. A hammer is also required in order to tap the taper pins firmly home when re-assembling the movement.

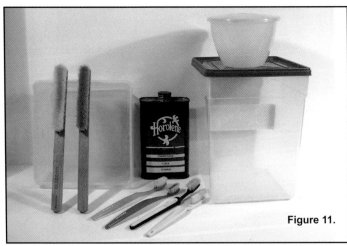

Figure 11.

Figure 12.

Figure 10 shows a couple of watchmaker's loupes and a pair of tweezers. Although not essential when dismantling or reassembling a clock movement, the close inspection of the plates, pivots and wheels is paramount in order to check they are perfectly clean before putting the movement back together. The tweezers are of great help in guiding the pivots into their respective holes when re-assembling the movement.

When cleaning the movement special clock brushes can be bought, but old toothbrushes will work just as well.

If immersing the plates and components in cleaning fluid some sort of container is required, preferably one with a lid. **Figure 11** shows a tin of concentrated clock cleaner, several containers and brushes, all suitable for the purpose.

Apart from cleaning fluid the only materials the absolute beginner is likely to require are some bundles of pegwood, oil, and replacement steel pins. Invariably the old tapered movement pins become badly marked and require replacing with new ones.

Graded assortments of pins are available from the material suppliers. It is bad workmanship to replace badly mauled or ill fitting pins. All these items are shown in **figure 12**. The pegwood is used to clean the pivot holes and requires 'sharpening', however wooden cocktail sticks work just as well and come ready sharpened!

Always buy the correct grade of oil for the job in hand. Small movements only require light clock oil; larger movements and mainsprings require heavier grades.

The oil can be applied with special spear-pointed 'oilers'; however, depending on the size of the pivot, the blade of a very small watchmaker's screwdriver can be used as long as it is kept clean. Always keep the oil free from dust and out of direct sunlight.

The tools mentioned above are all that should be required for the dismantling and cleaning of a simple clock movement. As your skill and interest grows and you take on more complicated movements and repairs, other tools will naturally be required.

CHAPTER 3
DISMANTLING

Before removing the movement from the case the pendulum should be removed to avoid damaging the suspension spring. The pendulum is simply unhooked from the suspension. The hands should then be removed. The hands are held in place with a tapered cross pin and domed 'collet' shown in **figure 13**. The pin should be removed

spring removed from the back cock. The mainspring *must* be let down before removing the front plate of the movement. The clockmaker uses a special mainspring letting-down tool, which I strongly urge anyone who envisages working on spring-driven clocks to buy and use. As the beginner is unlikely to own a commercial letting-

Figure 13.

Figure 14.

Figure 15.

using a pair of flat pliers. By placing one jaw of the pliers against the smallest diameter of the pin and the other jaw against the end of the centre arbor, closing the jaws should dislodge the pin. The hands can then be removed from the dial. The hour hand is a push or friction fit on its pipe and should be eased gently, avoiding damage to the dial.

The movement can now be removed from the case and the suspension

down tool I will describe an alternative and safe method of letting down the mainspring. A pipe cleaner is inserted between the crossings of the escape wheel and twisted around one of the movement pillars. In effect this secures the escape wheel and locks the wheel train. The movement back cock is then unscrewed and removed along with the pallets.

The pipe cleaner is then untwisted

and removed from the escape wheel, at the same time finger pressure is applied to the escape wheel arbor and the train is allowed to run down slowly until the mainspring is fully unwound. Do not allow the wheel train to run at speed as this could score the arbor pivots.

With the mainspring completely unwound, the motionwork, ratchet wheel, ratchet click and click spring shown in **figure 14** can now be safely removed. The movement should be laid on its back and the taper pins securing the front plate to the movement pillars removed. The front plate should then be lifted *evenly* from the pillars. If the front plate is lifted

with the aid of a small screwdriver. The winding arbor should be reversed slightly in order to disengage the winding arbor hook from the eye in the inner-coils of the mainspring. The arbor is then removed from the barrel as shown in **figure 17**.

The mainspring should be removed from the barrel prior to cleaning, however this requires the use of a mainspring winder. On no account should the spring be removed by hand. Removing springs by hand is both dangerous to the operator and may cause damage to both the barrel and the spring. If you do not possess or are not familiar or confident with the

Figure 16.

Figure 17.

unevenly there is the risk of damaging the finer pivots of the arbors. The movement at this stage is shown in **figure 15**.

The wheelwork can then be removed from the back plate.

The dismantled movement is shown in **figure 16**.

Before cleaning the movement the mainspring should be inspected. The barrel cover is provided with a small slot and the cover should be prised off

operation of a mainspring winder and the removal of clock mainsprings, I strongly suggest that you take the barrel to a professional clockmaker and ask him to remove the spring for you. On no account should you try to remove the spring yourself without the correct equipment and know-how.

Clock mainsprings can be very dangerous to work with and even when using the correct equipment you must

Figure 18.

always be vigilant. Eye protection should be worn at all times and substantial protective gloves should be used. Always treat mainsprings with the respect they deserve.

Figure 18 shows the movement completely dismantled and ready for cleaning.

When the spring is removed if it is damaged in any way or fatigued it should be replaced. Springs can become exhausted or what is termed 'barrel bound' and hence lose their efficiency.

16

CHAPTER 4
CLEANING

There are many commercial products on the market for cleaning clock movements, each one with its own advantages and disadvantages.

A good all-round movement cleaner and one that I have used for many years is Horolene. This is a water-based ammonia solution sold in a concentrated form. In its diluted state it is a relatively

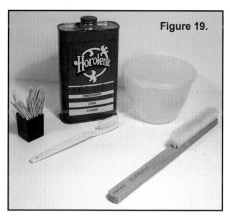

Figure 19.

low concentrate ammonia product. It is readily available, easy to use, and is relatively inexpensive.

As with all chemical solutions, the instructions must be read and adhered to, and the product when used disposed of in a responsible manner. All the dismantled components of the movement except the mainspring should be fully immersed in the made-up solution, which should be used in a container with a tight-fitting lid. **Figure 19** shows a small can of Horolene, a suitable container, some

brushes and cocktail sticks.

As the solution is ammonia based, care should be taken not to breathe in the fumes, and the cleaning should take place in a well-ventilated room. Rubber gloves should be used and care taken not to let the product come in contact with the skin or eyes.

The dismantled components are allowed to stand in the solution until the ammonia dissolves the dirt and tarnish. Light agitation with a toothbrush at 10-minute intervals can be beneficial in removing stubborn stains and dirt. The components should not be immersed in the cleaning solution for longer than half an hour, and sufficient of the fluid should be used to totally cover the components in order to avoid a 'tide-mark'.

The components should then be well rinsed in warm clean water and thoroughly dried. The plates and wheelwork *etc*, can be seen before and after in **figures 20, 21** and **22**. An electric hand-held hair dryer can be used to speed up the drying process.

All the pivot holes in both movement plates should be cleaned out with pegwood from both sides of the plate. Wooden cocktail sticks work perfectly well in the smaller pivot holes and small pieces of dowel whittled to a point can be used in the larger holes.

The wheelwork and plates can now be brushed with a soft toothbrush or clock brush, and it is surprising what can be achieved with a little elbow grease!

Figure 20.

The brushes can be periodically cleaned on a block of chalk. Any rust on the steel arbors or pinion leaves can be removed with fine emery papers prior to polishing with a proprietary metal polishing paste such as Autochrome metal polish. All traces of the polishing medium should be removed and the components brought to a high polish.

The mainspring should be washed in paraffin. Fine wire wool can be used to remove any congealed oil or dirt. Take care not to distort the spring whilst cleaning. The spring should finally be washed in fresh paraffin and left to dry.

Figure 21.

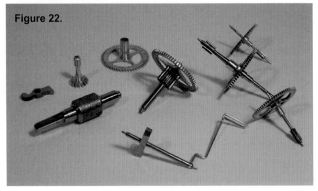

Figure 22.

CHAPTER 5
RE-ASSEMBLY

Figure 23.

Figure 24.

Re-assembly of the movement is fairly straightforward. Firstly the mainspring should be replaced in the barrel. If a clockmaker removed the spring for you, the spring and barrel should be returned in order for him to refit the spring. The winding arbor is inserted in the barrel and a check made to ensure the inner coil of the spring is satisfactorily hooked on to the arbor. The inner coil of the spring should be a snug fit around the arbor as seen in **figure 23**. The spring should be lubricated with heavy grade clock oil. Capillary action will ensure the oil coats the inner coils of the spring. The barrel cover should be tapped home using a wooden block and hammer. The barrel should be rested on the open soft jaws of a vice and the barrel protected with a soft cloth as shown in **figure 24**. Ensure the barrel cap is

replaced the correct way up and check the mainspring is still securely hooked on to the winding arbor after fitting the cap. The barrel arbor pivots should be lubricated where they run in the barrel, **figure 25**.

The barrel and wheelwork can then be replaced in the back plate of the movement as shown in **figure 26**.

The front plate should then be gently fitted in place over the pillars. It will be found necessary to guide the pivots of the arbors into their respective pivot holes in the top plate with tweezers. At the same time only very gentle downward pressure should be maintained on the front plate. Take great care with the third and escape wheel pivots as these are very fine and could be easily bent or broken. When all the pivots are located in the front plate, the plate should be seat positively against

Figure 25.

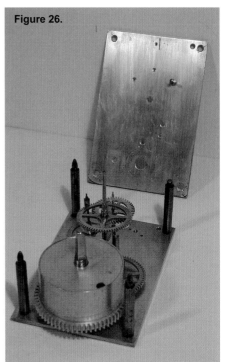

Figure 26.

Figure 27.

Figure 28.

20

the shoulders of the pillars. The plate can be firmly pinned to the pillars with tapered steel clock pins.

The pins should be tapped home with a small hammer.

With the plates pinned-up there should be a noticeable end-shake between the shoulders of the arbors and the movement plates.

By applying pressure with a thumb to the great wheel, the train of wheels should run freely and gradually coast to a halt. Any sudden stoppage should be investigated.

The pallets and back cock should be fitted in place. Light clock oil should then be applied to the pivots on the front and back plate. A darning needle or the tip of a very fine watchmaker's screwdriver can make a suitable oiler.

Oil is not applied to the teeth of the wheels of pinions. Capillary action will ensure the oil runs into the pivot hole in the plate. Be careful not to use too much oil. Surplus oil will only run down the plates and attract dirt and dust. The motionwork should be fitted to the front plate and the ratchet wheel, ratchet click and spring should be replaced. Both the ratchet wheel and click should be oiled. The pendulum suspension should be replaced and the mainspring can then be wound up with the clock key.

Light oil should be applied to the faces of the pallets, and the slot where the suspension spring passes through the pendulum crutch.

The suspension must not bind in the slot but equally there should not be too much play.

It is always a good idea to test the movement before re-fixing the movement in the clock case.

The movement should be hung vertically, and the pendulum hung on the suspension. It may be necessary to set the clock in beat.

To set the clock in beat and produce an even tick, the pendulum crutch may require bending slightly to the left or right, **figure 27**. It should be possible to adjust the crutch between the thumb and first finger. The crutch is adjusted until an even beat or tick is obtained.

Even after just cleaning the movement, you should notice an improvement in the action of the escapement and the life of the clock.

Of course simple cleaning will not remedy any major faults, but it is surprising what a good clean and re-oil can do, especially with a movement that has not been used for some time. The re-assembled and cleaned movement can be seen in **figure 28**.

Finally the movement should be fitted into the case.

It may be necessary to adjust the beat once more, as sometimes the movements are not always fitted perfectly vertical in the case. There is nothing more irritating than listening to a clock out of beat.

With the dial in place the timekeeping of the clock can be checked accurately and the pendulum bob adjusted to give a good rate. The bob is screwed upwards if the clock is losing, and downwards if the clock is gaining.

CHAPTER 6
RE-BUSHING I

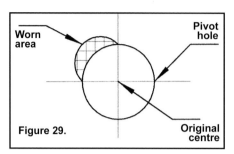

Figure 29.

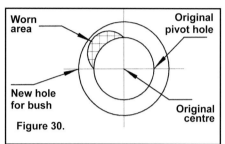

Figure 30.

If a clock movement is not cleaned and oiled at regular intervals some components are bound to wear and eventually the clock will stop.

In a spring-driven clock the motive power from the going barrel is transmitted to the escapement via the train wheels. If the pivot holes in the movement plates are allowed to become excessively dirty, the mixture of dirt and oil and other hard particles embedded in the brass plates combine to create a compound which will wear both the actual pivot of the arbor and the hole in which the pivot runs. The resulting wear of the pivot holes can eventually become so bad as to lead to a misalignment in the

depthing of the wheels and pinions and subsequently a substantial reduction in the power being delivered to the escape wheel.

When a clock is dismantled the pivots and pivot holes should be closely examined.

Any scored or damaged pivots should be repaired, and any oval or elongated pivot holes re-bushed.

It is difficult in words to describe exactly when a pivot hole requires re-bushing, however if the pivots are visibly sloppy in their holes, or if the pivot hole is worn by about a quarter of its diameter then it probably needs re-bushing.

Any damaged arbor pivots should be

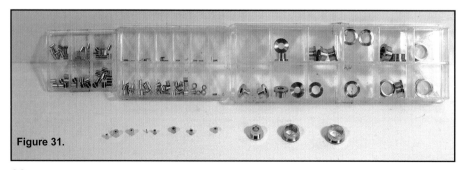

Figure 31.

Figure 32.

attended to first and must be returned to a parallel condition with no ridges or scoring.

The efficient repair of pivots requires the use of a lathe. As the beginner is unlikely to own a suitable lathe with the necessary attachments and tools, I suggest any damaged pivots be taken to a qualified clock repairer who will posses both the required skills and equipment.

Any repaired pivots will have to be re-polished and this can reduce the diameter of the pivot quite substantially, therefore the pivot holes in the movement plates must not be re-bushed until after the pivots have been attended to.

The worn pivot hole is best inspected with a loupe. In order to correct the wear the pivot hole is opened with a tapered cutting broach before inserting a suitable brass bush.

The principal object of the repair is to reinstate the centre of the original pivot hole in the movement plate in order to ensure the correct alignment and depthing of the wheel teeth and pinions.

Figure 29 shows a sketch of a worn pivot hole. The shaded area represents the wear that has taken place.

By careful examination of the pivot hole it should be possible to visually ascertain the direction of the wear. The hole is opened from the inside of the plate until a bush can be hammered in

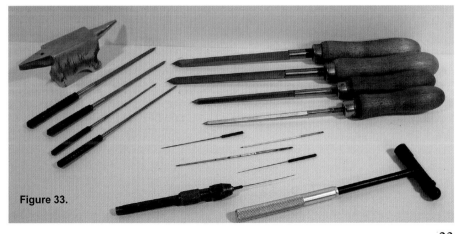

Figure 33.

23

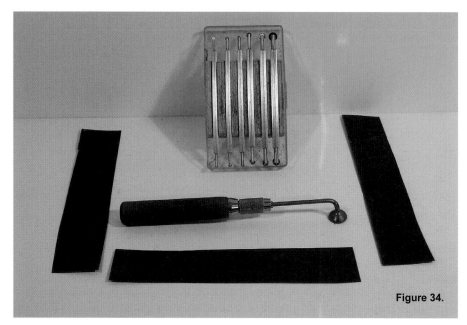

Figure 34.

place. The hole for the bush must be central in relation to the original centre of the pivot hole as shown in **figure 30**.

Commercial bushes are available in a variety of sizes for different types of clock movement.

Figures 31 and **32** show a varied selection of brass bushes for use on clocks ranging from small mantel clocks to longcase clocks.

You can see all the bushes are of differing diameters, heights and pivot hole sizes. Both tapered and parallel bushes are obtainable in most sizes. I would recommend the beginner choose parallel bushes to start with. You will require a good assortment of five-sided tapered cutting broaches, a small hammer and a steel stake or anvil. All these items are shown in **figure 33**.

Some of the broaches are quite large and fitted with wooden handles; these are for use on large movements such as those of longcase clocks. The other smaller broaches suitable for mantel clocks can be held in pin vices if necessary. It is sometimes difficult to obtain a commercial bush that exactly matches the thickness of the movement plate. When fitted, the bush must not be left proud of the plate and may have to be reduced in height; also a countersink or oil sink may have to be provided on the outside of the plate. With this in mind a bulls-foot file and some sheets of emery papers as well as the rotary countersinks shown in **figure 34** will be found useful.

24

CHAPTER 7
RE-BUSHING II

In order to re-bush a worn pivot hole a suitable size of bush must first be selected. The bush should be at least the same height as the thickness of the movement plate, and as a general rule the outside diameter of the bush should be at least double the diameter of the pivot. The pivot hole in the bush should be just under the diameter of the pivot.

If the worn pivot hole in the plate is of a reasonable size and worn badly oval, the hole should first be 'drawn' or filed by an equal amount in the opposite direction using a small round file. This is represented in the drawing shown in **figure 35**.

If the pivot hole is very small this is not always possible. Should this be the case, commence broaching the pivot hole using slightly more pressure on the unworn side of the hole at first to even up the wear.

The broach will then centre itself in the original hole.

The broaching is done from the inside of the plate and the broach must be kept upright and square to the plate as shown in **figure 36**. This is very important if the bush is to fit correctly.

Keep inspecting the plate both horizontally and vertically in order to check that the broach is being used upright. Use the broach in one direction only and do not use too much pressure, which will only jam the broach in the hole.

The hole should be frequently checked,

and the broaching continued until the bush will just enter the tapered hole in the plate as shown in **figure 37**. It may well be found that the broaching has thrown up a slight burr which should be removed with the rotary countersink.

The plate should be placed on a polished steel stake and the bush gently hammered in place from the inside of the plate. When the bush impacts with the stake, the continued hammering will expand it in the plate and ensure a

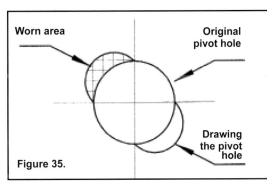

Figure 35.

positive and tight fit in the hole.

With the bush in place any surplus height must be removed from the inside of the plate with the bulls-foot file. Take great care not to accidentally mark and scratch the surface of the plate. The height of the bush must be reduced until it is flush with the plate. Finally very fine emery papers should be used and when finished you should not be able to detect the bush in the plate. The new pivot hole is then opened with a cutting

Figure 36.

Figure 37.

shown in **figure 39**.

Again the work is brought to a good finish and the new bush should not be visible in the plate. Finally the pivot hole

is opened from the inside of the plate to fully accept the pivot.

Whilst broaching the pivot hole progress should be frequently checked with the pivot. Again the broach must be kept upright whilst cutting the pivot

broach until the pivot will just enter the start of the hole. Again the broach must be kept upright whilst opening the hole. **Figure 38** shows the inside of the plate and the new pivot hole. If a countersink is to be made on the outside of the plate this should be cut now. Countersinks are not always found an all clock plates and should only be provided if in keeping with the rest of the movement.

The rotary countersink is used and the countersink on the outside of the plate is

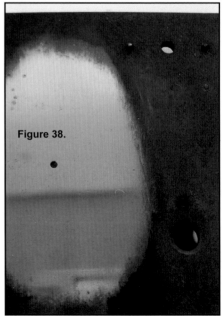

Figure 38.

Figure 39.

hole. The pivot hole can be very lightly countersunk in order to remove any burrs thrown up by the broaching.

The wheel and arbor should be tried between both plates and the plates should be tightly pinned in place. The wheel should spin freely and there should be a noticeable amount of free end-shake between the shoulders of the arbor and the plates. Any lack of end-shake or sudden stoppage of the wheel indicates a tight pivot. When happy with the running of the wheel and arbor, the adjacent wheels of the train should be fitted between the plates in order to check the depthing of the wheel with its corresponding pinion/wheel.

The wheels should all spin freely coasting to a gradual halt with no sudden stoppages or halting of the train.

27

CHAPTER 8
THE ESCAPEMENT

Having discussed damaged arbor pivots and looked at the re-bushing of worn pivot holes, the next component to inspect when dismantling a clock movement is the escapement, and in particular the impulse faces of the pallets. Both pallets are in almost constant contact with the teeth of the escape wheel and are prone to wear and pitting.

Figure 40 shows the relationship of the pallets with the escape wheel. As you can see there must be an element of freedom or 'drop' between the impulse faces of the pallets and the teeth of the escape wheel in order for the escape wheel to turn and travel through the pallets. The drop is the amount of freedom between the release of one tooth from the entry pallet to the arrest of another tooth by the exit pallet. In a well-regulated escapement the amount of drop should be minimal, ensuring that the maximum driving force of the escape wheel is used to impulse the pallets/pendulum and keep the clock running.

Although the acting faces of the pallets are usually made from hardened steel, the constant action of the escape wheel teeth on the pallets can cause pitting

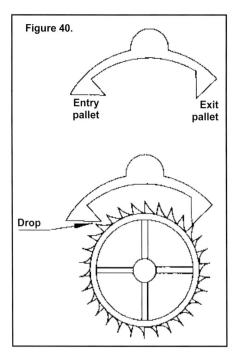

Figure 40.

Entry pallet

Exit pallet

Drop

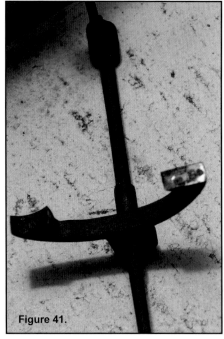

Figure 41.

or grooving which has the effect of increasing the drop of the escapement.

If the drops between the escape wheel teeth and the face of the pallets become too great, a lot of the power of the escape wheel is lost, resulting in insufficient power being provided to keep the pendulum oscillating and the clock running.

Figure 41 shows the entry pallet from a longcase clock and the surface pitting can be seen on the face of the pallet. In order to reverse the wear and reinstate the correct action of the escapement the pitting on both pallets has to be removed and the surface of the pallets brought back to their original state.

One of the simplest ways of achieving this is to soft solder on each pallet a strip of spring steel.

A suitable strip of spring steel is selected and the face of the pallet reduced by the thickness of the spring steel. As the pallets are usually dead hard they will have to be annealed so they can be filed or alternatively the damaged pallets can be stoned or ground away.

The faces of the pallets must be reduced by *exactly* the same thickness of the replacement spring otherwise the resulting drop will be either too great or too shallow. The angles of the pallets must be maintained.

The face of one of the pallets after filing is shown in **figure 42**. You can see some traces of pitting still remain, as the wear to the pallets was greater than the thickness of spring I was using in the repair.

Both the steel facing and the pallet are then tinned with soft solder. Finally the facing is soldered in place as shown in **figure 43** and any surplus material removed from the edges of the pallets.

Figure 42.

Figure 43.

Figure 44.

File or grind any overhanging material in the direction of the pallet in order to avoid tearing the new facing off the pallet. The face of the pallet should be brought to a high polish as shown in **figure 44**.

The pallets should then be tried in the movement, and the escape wheel and pallets checked right around the wheel. The drop for each tooth on both the entry and exit pallets should be minimal, and the same on both pallets.

CHAPTER 9
THE MAINSPRING

Figure 45.

When overhauling a spring-driven clock the mainspring should always be removed, inspected and cleaned. A mainspring winder must be used when removing or replacing clock mainsprings.

Never be tempted to remove the springs by hand. This is dangerous to the repairer and can cause damage to both the spring and the movement. **Figure 45** shows a traditional clock mainspring winder. The winder in use, removing a spring from a going barrel is shown in **figure 46**. Eye protection and suitable protective gloves should be worn at all times when working with clock mainsprings.

Always read the instructions provided with the mainspring winder and familiarise yourself with the working procedures and operation of the equipment.

If the spring is contained in a going barrel, over the years the spring can become fatigued or 'set'.

A fatigued spring is inefficient and will be unable to deliver sufficient power to drive the clock for its full period of time.

After removing the barrel cover the spring should be inspected and if the spring is in good condition it should appear similar to **figure 47A**. All the coils of the spring should be contained tightly against the wall of the barrel and only the centre coil attached to the winding arbor should project across the inside of the barrel. At **figure 47B** the coils of the spring extend fully into the centre of the barrel, indicating a fatigued spring.

The mainspring should be removed

Figure 46.

and if found to be in good condition the spring should be cleaned in paraffin. Any old sticky oil can be removed with the aid of wire wool. However if the spring is fatigued it should be discarded and replaced.

Replacement mainsprings are obtained from the material suppliers and the required dimensions can be taken from the old spring. The necessary measurements are the springs *height*, *thickness* and *length*.

Springs from going barrels have an eye in the tail of the spring, however open springs (not contained in a barrel) have a loop end.

Sometimes, in a spring fitted to a going barrel, the eye in tail of the spring becomes torn as shown in **figure 48**. If the spring is in otherwise good condition it is possible to repair the spring. If the eye in the inner coil of the spring is torn the spring should be replaced. It is

dangerous and very difficult to repair the inner coils of a clock mainspring.

The damaged eye in the tail of the spring should be cut from the spring with a pair of cutters. Only remove the damaged area of the spring. The spring should be shortened as little as possible.

Holding the spring in a pair of pliers, the end of the spring should be held in the flame of a gas torch until cherry red. Try to avoid any other parts of the spring becoming hot. Gradually remove the end of the spring from the flame allowing it to cool slowly. The softened steel can then be centre punched in the centre of the spring, prior to drilling with a small drill.

The hole in the spring is then opened out to a suitable shape with a needle file and the sharp edges on the end of the spring rounded off. The finished repair is shown in **figure 49**.

The spring must be replaced in the barrel with the mainspring winder. With

32

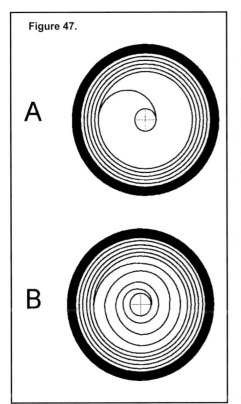

Figure 47.

A

B

Figure 48.

Figure 49.

the spring safely in the barrel the spring should be oiled. The edges of the coiled spring should be oiled with a grade of oil suitable for mainsprings. Capillary action will ensure the surface of the spring becomes lubricated during use.

CHAPTER 10
THE PENDULUM

Figure 50.

On the vast majority of domestic pendulum clocks the pendulum is detachable from the movement and is usually suspended from a suspension cock attached to the back plate of the movement.

The actual suspension from which the pendulum hangs is usually made from spring steel, however this is not always the case. Some early French clocks employed a silk thread from which to suspend the pendulum. **Figure 50** shows a silk suspension and the special light pendulum used for these clocks. Most spring steel suspensions are fitted with a top and bottom block made from brass. The top block attaches to the suspension cock and the lower block carries a pin on to which the pendulum hooks. On longcase clocks and on some other types of clock the suspension spring is attached to the actual pendulum. With most mantel clocks the pendulum is usually separate from the suspension and normally hooks on to the bottom block of the suspension spring. A group of typical suspensions for mantel clocks can be seen in **figure 51** and the suspension for a longcase clock is shown in **figure 52**.

The suspension cock must be firmly attached to the movement and the actual suspension spring must be positively located in the suspension cock. The suspension spring must hang vertically

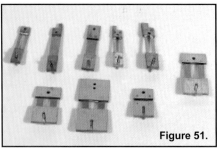

Figure 51.

Figure 52.

Figure 53.

without any kinks, tears or creases and it must not be 'set' in any direction. If the spring becomes damaged or corroded it should be replaced. Replacement suspension springs for most types of clocks can be obtained from the material suppliers.

With a mantel clock the top block of the suspension is usually held in place with a removable steel pin or positively located as part of the suspension cock assembly.

The pendulum should hook on to the lower block of the suspension without any play, and the pendulum rod should be a sliding fit in the fork of the pendulum crutch. A pendulum fitted to a French mantel clock movement can be seen in **figure 53**.

As the pendulum oscillates the rod rises and falls very slightly in the fork of the crutch, **figure 54**, and any binding here can be sufficient to stop the clock. On the other hand there should not be

35

Figure 54.

excessive play between the pendulum rod and the fork in the crutch. Too much freedom will result in a loss of motive power to the pendulum and the failure of the movement to keep the pendulum oscillating.

The suspension should allow the pendulum to swing in one plane only and the pendulum should not wobble or roll.

With a longcase pendulum the whole of the lower block of the suspension must fit the fork or aperture in the crutch exactly. If the sides of the block are not perfectly parallel to the fork, or the block is too small there will be a tendency for the block to twist in the fork, and set up a corresponding motion to the pendulum.

The pendulum rod should not be bent or misshapen in any way and the pendulum bob should be a good sliding fit on its block. The rating nut should run easily on the threads in order to adjust the bob and the timekeeping of the clock. In order for the escapement to function correctly, the movement of a pendulum clock must be level. If this is not the case the 'beat' will be uneven and the clock will stop.

Most domestic clocks are set in beat by bending the pendulum crutch slightly to the left or right until an even tick is obtained. Some French and German clocks are fitted with a friction fit between the pendulum crutch and pallet arbor. With these clocks adjustment is much simpler and the crutch is simply 'pushed' slightly to the left or right in order to put the clock in beat.

CHAPTER 11
RACK STRIKING

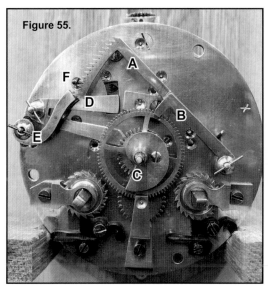

Figure 55.

Figure 56.

Striking movements are no more difficult to repair than simple timepiece movements however they do require a little more work when re-assembling as they must be set up correctly if they are to function reliably. A striking movement employs a second, separate train of wheels, which are released by the motionwork of the clock movement. A second mainspring powers the train, and the wheels and arbors are usually placed to the left of the going train.

A clock with a striking movement usually strikes once on the half-hour and the number of hours on the hour. Most domestic striking clocks are fitted with either rack or countwheel striking.

The names are derived from the rack or countwheel, which are totally different components used to control the number of hours the clock strikes. There are advantages and disadvantages to both systems, but when properly set-up and working correctly both systems are efficient and reliable.

A French rack striking movement with the dial removed is shown in **figure 55**. The rack, from which the mechanism takes its name can be clearly seen at *A* along with other component parts of the strikework.

The names of the other components are as follows.

Figure 57.

Figure 58.

A: Rack
B: Rack tail
C: Hour snail
D: Lifting lever
E: Rack hook
F: Gathering pallet

Some of the components are attached to arbors and wheels, which run between the movement plates shown in **figure 56**.

The different arbors and wheels are named as follows.

G: Fly
H: Warning wheel
I: Gathering pallet wheel
J: Strike stop arm
K: Pin wheel
L: Hammer arbor.

There are two pins fitted opposite each other on the rear of the cannon pinion, which, via the lifting lever, D, release the striking mechanism of the movement. In **figure 55** you can see the lower arm

of the lifting lever located behind the cannon pinion.

The cannon pinion makes one complete revolution every hour. One of the pins is fitted slightly nearer the centre of the pinion and releases the train at the half-hour. The other pin releases the train on the hour.

As the hour pin on the cannon pinion approaches the hour, the pin lifts the lifting lever, which in turn via a pin in the rack hook raises the rack hook, E. The rack hook disengages from the rack and the rack falls until the rack tail, B, contacts the snail, C. The snail is attached to the hour wheel and makes one complete revolution in 12 hours. If assembled correctly, at one o'clock the rack tail falls on the highest point of the snail, and at 12 o'clock, the lowest.

Clearly, as the hour wheel and snail revolve, at each hour the rack tail falls on a progressively smaller diameter of snail. The more the rack falls, the more teeth the gathering pallet, F, gathers and

38

Figure 59.

Figure 60.

the greater the number of hours struck by the clock. Each tooth of the rack when gathered by the gathering pallet represents one hammer blow.

The rack hook is made with a square hole which fits on to the strike stop arm arbor, *J*. As the rack hook is raised, and the rack released, simultaneously the stop arm releases the stop pin on the gathering pallet wheel, *I*, allowing the train to run. However the train does not run very far as the pin on the warning wheel, *H*, is arrested by a protrusion on the lifting lever which protrudes through an aperture cut in the front plate of the movement. This sequence of events takes place usually three or four minutes before the hour or half-hour, and is commonly known as 'the warning'. Only when the lifting lever completely falls from the pin on the cannon pinion does the striking commence, and the gathering pallet gathers the teeth on the rack. Whilst striking, the rack keeps the rack hook raised and the stop arm clear of the stop

pin on the gathering pallet wheel.

As the striking train runs, the pins on the pin wheel, *K*, engage with a pin fitted to the hammer arbor, *L*, causing the hammer to strike the bell or gong.

When the gathering pallet has gathered all the teeth of the rack, the rack hook drops and at the same time the stop arm engages with the stop pin on the gathering pallet wheel, arresting the strike.

The process is the same at the half-hour, only as the pin on the cannon pinion is nearer the centre of the pinion it does not raise the lifting lever as far. The lifting lever is raised far enough for the rack hook to release the strike stop arm and free the striking train, but not far enough to disengage the rack hook from the rack and allow the rack to drop. Once the pin on the cannon pinion releases the lifting lever which in turn frees the warning wheel, the gathering pallet makes one revolution, striking the bell or gong once before the train is again locked by the strike stop arm.

The fly, *G*, is simply an air brake, fitted to govern the speed of the striking.

In **figure 57** you can see the movement is about to strike the half-hour. The lifting lever has been lifted sufficiently to allow the train to run to warning, but not enough to disengage the rack hook from the rack and allow the rack tail to fall on to the snail. In **figure 58** the lifting lever has fallen, allowing the lifting lever to release the pin on the warning wheel and the movement to strike once at the half-hour.

In **figure 59** the movement is about to strike the hour. Here the lifting lever has lifted much further and not only has the movement run to warning, but the rack hook has disengaged from the rack allowing the rack tail to fall on to the snail. In **figure 60** the lifting lever has fallen and the gathering pallet is about to gather the teeth on the rack and the movement strike the designated number of hours.

CHAPTER 12
DISMANTLING AND ASSEMBLY

Before dismantling the movement, both mainsprings must be let down. The back cock and pallets can then be removed along with the hammer. Depending on the movement there may be a cross-pin retaining the hammer in place on its arbor. The striking work on the front plate should then be removed, starting with the rack. The minute cock, minute wheel and hour wheel can then be removed, followed by the cannon pinion, rack hook and lifting lever.

The gathering pallet is usually just a taper push fit on the gathering pallet arbor.

Take great care when easing the pallet from the arbor. The pallet should be levered up using two levers from the underside of the pallet. Never try to remove the pallet with a pair of pliers or

Figure 61.

Figure 62.

Figure 63.

Figure 64.

using leverage from one side of the pallet only. This is likely to result in a bent or broken arbor.

The ratchets, ratchet wheels, ratchet cocks and ratchet springs can then be removed.

The back plate can then be un-pinned and the wheels removed. It is usually easier to remove the wheels and arbors from the striking train first, followed by the going train. Any arbor return springs should be unscrewed and removed.

When dismantling a striking movement it is a good idea to keep the wheels, springs and barrels from each train separate from one another.

I always use separate marked containers in which to keep the component parts and wheels from each train. This avoids the need to actually mark the barrels, springs, barrel arbors *etc* in order to identify them.

The repairs and cleaning methods for a striking movement are just the same as those for a timepiece movement. Considering that some of the wheels

and arbors of the striking train run at considerably faster speeds and under different loads to the going train, the wear to the arbor pivots and pivot holes is generally the same. It does however pay to check the hammer arbor pivot holes for excessive wear.

The hammer arbor is usually fitted with a return spring. If the spring is particularly strong or badly positioned it can lead to these pivots wearing badly. All the pivots along with the pivot holes should be inspected and any worn holes re-bushed. The mainsprings should be removed and cleaned and the pallets and escapement inspected.

Unlike a simple timepiece movement whereby the going train can be assembled in any order, the wheels and arbors of a striking train must be assembled with reference to one-another if the striking mechanism is to function reliably.

The wheel trains including the barrels should be replaced in the front plate of the movement. Do not forget to include the hammer arbor and strike stop arm

Figure 65.

arbor. When re-assembling any striking movements there are two 'golden rules' which must be obeyed.

1. When assembled, and with the striking train locked, the hammer pin on the hammer arbor must be free of the pins on the pinwheel.

2. There must be half a turn of run on the warning wheel before the warning pin encounters the projection on the strike-lifting lever. On French movements sometimes the warning wheel and gathering pallet pinion are marked for reference when re-assembling the movement.

One leaf of the gathering pallet pinion has a small chamfer cut into the edge of a leaf, and the warning wheel is marked with a dot between two teeth. The cut pinion should mesh with the dot on the wheel if the run to warning is to be correct. However many striking trains are not marked, so the run to warning is checked and adjusted later on.

When replacing the back plate work from the barrel arbors upwards to the fly.

Ease the pivots into their respective pivot holes with tweezers and never apply force, especially with the fine pivots at the top of the train.

When you are sure the pivots are located correctly the back plate can be pinned in place.

In order to check the strike is set up correctly the rack and rack hook should be fitted on the front plate.

With the rack fully gathered the striking train should be made to run by hand until the pin on the gathering pallet wheel encounters the stop arm. With the train locked, the pin on the warning wheel should be just under the fly pinion, and the pin on the hammer arbor free from the pins on the pinwheel. The gathering pallet should now be fitted on to the gathering pallet arbor with the gathering edge of the pallet positioned uppermost and away from the teeth of the rack. The rack hook should be lifted and made to engage with two or three rack teeth. The train should then be run by hand and when the last tooth of the rack has been gathered, the train should lock and the pin on the hammer arbor should be free from the pins on the pinwheel. On French movements a separate removable cock is fitted to the back plate shown in **figure 61**. This cock can be unscrewed and the pinwheel disengaged from the gathering pallet pinion and adjusted until with the movement locked the hammer pin is free from the pinwheel. When the striking train locks, **figure 62**, the hammer pin should have just dropped off one of the pins on the pinwheel **figure 63**.

If a separate cock is not fitted, the movement plate must be unpinned and eased so the pinwheel and gathering pallet pinion can be re-meshed until correct. With this part of the striking train correct, the run of the warning wheel should be checked.

With the train locked, the pin on the warning wheel should be just under the fly pinion. If this is not the case, the plate should be unpinned and raised, and the meshing of the warning wheel pinion and gathering pallet wheel carefully disengaged and adjusted until this is so, **figure 64**.

It is very important that there is no more than half a turn of run on the warning wheel as otherwise the hammer will start to lift early, during the warning.

At all times when checking the strike, only power the train by hand; never be tempted to wind up the mainspring. Should the movement plates have to be separated, any power on the mainspring would result in damage to the movement.

When making any adjustments to the relationship of the wheels and pinions take great care not to strain or damage any of the arbors or pivots. Gently ease the plates and use tweezers to lift and disengage the arbors. Never use any force.

When the striking is correct the plates should be pinned up tightly and the gathering pallet positively located on its arbor. A hollow brass bush can be located over the gathering pallet and the pallet very gently tapped in place. Again, ensure the gathering edge of the pallet is uppermost and facing away from the teeth of the rack with the rack fully gathered and the striking train locked, **figure 65**. The rack and rack hook can then be removed.

CHAPTER 13
SETTING UP THE STRIKE

Having re-assembled all the internal wheelwork for the French rack striking movement, all the arbor pivots for both trains should now be lubricated with good clock oil before fitting the motionwork and striking levers. The lifting lever should be pinned in place and the cannon pinion fitted to the centre arbor. The rack and rack hook should also be pinned in place. I never oil the rack and lifting lever posts, but some repairers do. The barrel ratchets, clicks and springs should be replaced and oiled along with the pallets. The mainsprings

Figure 66.

can then be wound up.

Check that the return springs that operate on the hammer arbor and stop lever locate correctly on the arbors. It should now be possible to make an initial test of the striking action under power.

If the strike has been set up correctly, with the train locked, the pin on the hammer arbor should be free of the pins on the pinwheel and the pin on the warning wheel should be just under the fly pinion.

The motionwork must be set up accurately if the movement is to strike the hours correctly and at the correct time.

On most French rack striking clocks the cannon pinion, minute wheel and hour wheel are marked with dots indicating their positions in relation to each other. **Figure 66** shows the motionwork.

I have not fitted the minute wheel cock and I have removed the snail from the hour wheel for clarity.

The dots on each wheel should line up together as shown in **figure 66**.

The purpose of the dots is to ensure that the minute hand releases the striking train exactly on the hour and that the rack tail falls correctly on the snail.

If the motionwork is not provided with any indicating marks, the wheels should be set up so that the hour pin on

Figure 67.

the cannon pinion releases the lifting lever exactly on the hour, and that the rack tail falls on the lowest point of the snail. In **figure 67** you can see the minute hand is on the hour and the lifting lever and rack have fallen (12 o'clock). If the motionwork is set up in this way, thereafter all the other hours and half-hours will automatically be struck correctly.

Finally the hammer should be fitted on to the hammer arbor.

Always check the action of the hammer on the bell or gong. The hammerhead must not linger on, or double strike, the bell or gong.

The main advantage to rack striking is that owing to the snail being attached to the hour wheel there is no possibility of the striking sequence getting out of synchronisation at the hour.

The only disadvantage is that with rack striking if for some reason the strike fails, and the gathering pallet does not gather the rack, the rack tail will eventually jam with the snail at 12 o'clock and stop the clock.

Although not all rack-striking mechanisms are quite the same, most rack-striking movements follow a similar pattern and operate in a corresponding way.

46

CHAPTER 14
COUNTWHEEL STRIKING

Having looked at a French rack striking movement we will now take a look at a French countwheel striking movement.

Figure 68 shows the front plate of the movement with the dial removed and **figure 69** shows the back plate. A side view of the movement is given in **figure 70**.

The component parts of the strikework are as follows.

A. Lifting Lever
B. Locking lever
C. Locking knife
D. Countwheel
E. Fly
F. Warning wheel
G. Strike stop wheel
H. Pin wheel
I. Locking arbor
J. Stop arm
K. Hammer arbor

Two pins fitted to the rear of the cannon pinion activate the striking train by raising the lifting lever *A*. The pins on the cannon pinion are located opposite each other and unlike the pins on the rack striking movement both pins are at the same radius. One pin releases the train at the hour and the other at the half-hour. When lifted, the lifting lever raises the locking lever *B*, which is located on the

Figure 68.

locking arbor *I*. The locking arbor has a stop arm *J* which contacts a pin on the strike stop wheel *G*.

The raised stop arm via the locking arbor releases the strike stop wheel pin and the train starts to run. However the pin on the warning wheel *F* quickly encounters a projection on the lifting lever which protrudes through an aperture in the frontplate. The train is halted until the lifting lever falls from the pin on the cannon pinion, releasing the train exactly on the hour/half-hour.

The locking knife *C* is also part of the locking arbor. When the locking arbor is raised and the train starts to run, the edge of the locking knife runs on the rim of the countwheel *D*. You can see the rim of the countwheel is not continuous and has notches cut into it.

Figure 69.

Figure 70.

Whilst the locking knife is running on the rim of the wheel the knife keeps the stop arm on the locking arbor raised, and the train is free to run. The length of each ridge is made progressively longer and the movement is designed so the longest ridge allows the hammer to strike 12 blows at 12 o'clock. When the locking knife drops into the notch of the countwheel, the arm on the locking arbor falls and arrests the pin on the strike stop wheel, halting the strike.

The pinwheel H is geared to the countwheel arbor and as the pinwheel revolves the pin on the hammer arbor K is lifted and the hammer strikes the bell or gong.

As with the rack striking movement the fly E is an air brake, provided to regulate the speed of the striking.

The notches are provided not only to lock the train after the hour has struck, but also, the length of the notches are cut to allow for only one hammer blow to be struck at the half-hour.

When the knife-edge falls from the ridge on the countwheel the train should lock immediately. On the half-hour the pin on the cannon pinion raises the lifting lever and locking arbor, and the train runs to warning. When the lifting lever releases the train on the half-hour, the train runs but the locking knife is not raised by a ridge on the countwheel. Hence the stop lever is not raised and only allows one revolution of the stop wheel before the stop lever arrests the pin on the stop wheel. One revolution of the stop wheel represents one blow of the hammer. The countwheel has moved

Figure 71.

on slightly and the train is now locked with the knife-edge at the start of the next ridge. When the clock next strikes, the knife-edge will be raised and run on the ridge of the countwheel, striking the next number of hours.

After 12 o'clock the movement is required to strike once, three times. At 12.30, one o'clock and 1.30.

In order for this to take place the notch after the 12 o'clock ridge is cut longer than the notches between the other hours. **Figure 71** shows the countwheel, and the differing ridges and notches can be clearly seen. The 12 and 2 o'clock ridges have been labelled

The movement is dismantled and repaired in the same manner as the rack striking movement. Only the re-assembly

and setting up of the strike is different. Having attended to any repairs and cleaning of the French countwheel striking movement, the wheels and arbors should be replaced between the movement plates. This process is just the same as for the French rack striking movement.

CHAPTER 15

SETTING UP THE COUNTWHEEL

Figure 72.

Figure 73.

It now only remains to set up the strike. The two 'golden rules' mentioned before apply to this movement as with all striking movements.

1. When assembled, and with the striking train locked, the hammer pin on the hammer arbor must be free of the pins on the pinwheel.

2. There must be half a turn of run on the warning wheel before the warning pin encounters the projection on the strike-lifting lever. On French movements sometimes the warning wheel and gathering pallet pinion are marked for reference when re assembling the movement.

One leaf of the gathering pallet pinion has a small chamfer cut into the edge of a leaf, and the warning wheel is marked with a dot between two teeth. The cut pinion should mesh with the dot on the wheel if the run to warning is to be correct. However many striking trains are not marked, so the run to warning is checked and adjusted later on.

With a countwheel movement, in order to check the action of the striking train, the lifting lever, cannon pinion, locking lever and countwheel should be fitted in place.

The lifting lever should be raised and the train powered by hand until the knife-edge of the locking arbor drops into a notch on the countwheel and the train is arrested. The train must be arrested by the stop arm exactly as the knife-edge falls into the notch of the countwheel. It may

until the pinwheel can be disengaged and adjusted. Always take great care when easing the plates. Use tweezers to lift and disengage the arbors in order not to damage any of the pivots and wheels.

When correct, the pin on the hammer arbor should have just come off a pin on the pinwheel as the train locks.

Figure 74.

Figure 75.

be necessary to remove the countwheel and try it on a different square in order to obtain the optimum result. With the train arrested and the knife-edge of the locking arbor at the start of a notch in the countwheel, the hammer pin must be free of the pins on the pinwheel. If this is not the case the removable cock fitted to the back plate of the movement should be removed, and the pinwheel pinion disengaged from the wheel on the countwheel arbor. The pinwheel should be adjusted until the pins are free from the hammer pin.

If the movement is not fitted with a removable cock, the plates must be eased

With the train still locked the pin on the warning wheel should be inspected and there should be half a turn of run on the warning wheel before the warning pin encounters the projection on the lifting lever.

Again, if the warning wheel needs adjusting the plates will have to be lifted and the warning wheel pinion and stop wheel adjusted until correct. On the rack striking movement, with the striking train arrested, the warning pin would be situated just under the fly pinion. With a countwheel movement this is not the case. The layout of the front plate and arbors is slightly different.

51

However, when set-up correctly there should be no more than half a turn of run on the warning wheel; otherwise the hammer may start to lift early, during the warning.

Unlike the rack striking movement, the motionwork on a countwheel movement does not require setting up in any particular way.

The striking is controlled by the countwheel, and the pins on the cannon pinion merely release the striking train on the hour and half-hour. This is one of the major disadvantages of a countwheel movement, in that if for any reason the striking does not synchronise with the hands the mechanism will not automatically correct itself and the hours or half-hours will remain incorrect until corrected manually.

The movement should be oiled in the same way as the rack striking movement.

If the striking train is set up correctly, the stop arm shown at A in **figure 72** should arrest the train the moment the knife-edge falls from the ridge on the countwheel, **figure 73**.

When arrested at the half-hour, **figure 74**, the knife-edge should be situated just before the next ridge on the countwheel. When striking the hour, **figure 75**, the knife-edge riding on the ridge keeps the stop arm raised and the train free to run.

Although there are many other different types of rack and countwheel movements to be found, the principles outlined with these two French movements are common to most striking clocks which strike both the hours and half-hours.

CHAPTER 16
CONCLUSIONS

Having worked your way through this book, hopefully you will be a little more confident regarding not only the dismantling and cleaning of a clock movement but also the setting-up of a striking movement.

Of course not all movements or striking systems are the same, and you are bound to encounter other movements, different, but similar in principle.

The repairs that were covered in the series are the common repairs that you would expect to have to perform when dismantling and servicing a mechanical clock. These repairs are necessary due to the normal wear and ageing of components.

People often forget that a clock is running 24 hours a day, 7 days a week, 52 weeks a year without a break. However well-made the clock may have been, working mechanical equipment will not last forever and at some time action has to be taken to repair the worn components and return the movement to working order.

These are what might be termed common everyday repairs, however you frequently find that you are called upon to perform unusual one-off repairs caused through accidental damage or misuse. This type of repair is much harder to advise upon, as each repair has to be assessed on the type of damage and also severity of the harm caused to the movement. No book or series of articles can hope to cover all eventualities, and here experience becomes your only guide.

With one-off repairs never be tempted to jump to conclusions or consider only one method of repair, always keep an open mind. The secret of effecting a successful repair lies in the combination of using the right materials, the correct technique and the proper tools. The beginner must never be tempted to take on any repairs whereby any of the three requisites outlined above are absent.

At the outset the newcomer is unlikely to possess all the tools he or she requires, however over the years as interest and experience grows more tools will be purchased and hand-in-hand the ability to perform more complex repairs will develop. There are very few secrets or repair techniques beyond the average practical person. Believe me, watchmakers and clockmakers are not wizards or rocket scientists, the vast majority are just patient thoughtful and dedicated workers.

However careful you are, things will go wrong; clock repairing is just like our everyday lives.

Wherever possible ensure that if possible your repairs are reversible, and that if things do go wrong it is feasible to redeem the situation. This is particularly relevant to the young beginner who lacks the years of experience and confidence of the old-timer. A lot of the time I find myself repairing other repairer's repairs. Usually this is because not enough thought has been given to the initial repair, or because of poor workmanship due to financial restraints.

This is not always the fault of the repairer, as it has to be said that at one time a lot of clock owners were very reluctant to pay the going rate for the job, or have their clocks repaired and serviced properly.

If you are unsure about what to do or how to perform a particular repair, initially don't do anything. Take advice, read up on the subject and if for any reason you are still unsure about what to do let someone else do the job. This does not always mean to say you have to let someone else do everything. It is perfectly acceptable to outsource a particular task to someone else until you are confident or have the necessary tools and know-how to do the job yourself.

When I first started repairing clocks I was very enthusiastic and particularly enjoyed cleaning and repairing carriage clocks; I took great delight in bringing the visible polished movements back to their original finish.

I was however terrified of working on platform escapements. At that time I would take the platforms to a local watchmaker who was very obliging and who would clean and service the platforms for me.

This arrangement became mutually

beneficial. Eventually when the watchmaker was convinced and confident that I knew what I was doing he would give me his carriage clocks to repair and clean (minus the platform) saving him a 'filthy job'.

In time, under the watchmaker's guidance, I became confident enough to work on the platforms myself; this mutual arrangement led to my apprenticeship in platform escapements!

Even now, lack of time sometimes prevents me doing all my restoration work myself.

I have just overhauled a 30-hour longcase clock: the countwheel pinion was missing and rather than set up the lathe for wheel cutting I purchased a pinion from a specialist wheel-cutter who had a correctly sized pinion in stock.

This was cost effective both in time and money.

Quite often wheels and pinions are found to be missing or damaged, I know many professionals who do not cut their own wheels and rely on others to do this job for them.

The beginner should try and examine as many different clock movements as possible in order to increase his knowledge of the different types of movements that have been produced over the years.

There is no substitute to actually seeing and handling a movement in order to understand how it works. Pictures are helpful, but a clearer understanding is easier to grasp when a mechanism is viewed as a whole. Despite the best endeavours of authors and publishers the relationship of the gearing and escapement, motionwork and strike-train can be confusing when depicted with one-dimensional diagrams or photographs.

Regarding general hand tools, always buy the best you can afford. I know this is often said, and ignored, but it is the best policy.

Specialist tools should be bought as required, after much thought.

It is possible to get carried away and spend all your money on expensive tools that you will use only once or twice.

If you intend working on spring-driven clocks a mainspring winder and letting down key is essential.

A depthing tool is usually only required for infrequent repairs, or in clock construction. A bushing tool can speed up the work and in some cases accuracy, but it only replicates what can be done with hand tools, which are far cheaper to buy.

Ultrasonic cleaning tanks are another item worth considering if you are going to clean a lot of filthy clocks: they certainly do a brilliant job, far better than hand cleaning, and they are good for delicate items which don't want handling too much.

I am often asked about lathes and wheel-cutting engines.

A lathe is very useful in that it increases the amount of components that you can actually make yourself, and very useful when working on pivots *etc*. However even a good second hand lathe and the necessary accessories will represent a considerable capital investment that you will have to weigh up.

In my opinion wheel-cutting engines are only of use to the clock constructor,

and even then I would rather cut my wheels on the lathe.

A lathe is far more rigid and it is possible to cut pinions on a lathe, which you cannot do with a wheel-cutting engine.

Clock repairing can become a very interesting and highly rewarding hobby. Requiring very little physical effort, it is suitable for both young and old alike.

As a hobby you are under no pressure to complete a job in any specific time. There are no production schedules to meet. You set the pace and determine the timescales involved.

This can lead to the dedicated enthusiast doing as good a job as the professional who has other commercial considerations to weigh up and consider.

Specialisation is another aspect of clock repairing which can be more open to the enthusiast than the professional. Generally the professional must diversify in order to attract as many customers as possible; the devotee can please himself in what he chooses to do.

I know many non-professional repairers who are very knowledgeable in specific fields of horology quite often neglected by the professional.

Finally having learned as much as you can from articles, books and general research, we are very fortunate in this country in having the British Horological Institute who hold courses in all aspects of clock and watch repair. These courses are diverse and open to both beginner and experienced alike.

APPENDIX 1
FAULT FINDING

When there is no apparent reason for a clock stopping or failing to run, the beginner is sometimes at a loss to know where to look to find the fault and effect a cure. There are many reasons for a clock stopping, some of the reasons are simple to spot, and others are not.

If a systematic check is made, this can help to pinpoint the fault and in some cases save a lot of unnecessary work.

It always pays to keep an open mind regarding the cause of possible faults.

If the clock does not belong to you, asking the owner some relevant questions can sometimes help.

You may also find that the obvious faults are not always the only reason for the clock stopping; though fortunately this is not always the case.

A friend had of mine owns a rather nice longcase clock which had just been overhauled; the clock had been moved whilst the decorators were wallpapering the hallway. After replacing the clock in exactly the same place, the clock refused to go. A simple examination revealed the problem. Whilst removing the movement from the case someone must have unknowingly caught and slightly bent the hour hand backwards. The hour hand was now catching on the tip of the seconds

With all timepiece and striking pendulum clocks check the movement is wound up and the clock is in beat. Ensure the pendulum is correctly located in the crutch and that the suspension is operating properly.

Pendulum clocks will not run if out of beat, or the pendulum/suspension is faulty in any way. The pendulum rod must not bind or be too loose between the forks of the crutch.

Check the hands are free of one another and move the minute hand back for 10 minutes.

If the hour, minute and seconds hands are catching as they pass they will stop the clock.

If the movement is a striking movement and the clock stops repeatedly at the same time the striking could have failed and be stopping the clock or the strike release mechanism could be responsible for stopping the clock.

Un-pin and remove the hands and the dial.

The dial may be obstructing the hands or interfering with the motionwork of the movement.

With just the hands fitted in place check there is a gap between the back of the bow spring and the front of the movement plate.

The back of the bow spring must not rub on the front of the movement plate.

A small extension to the centre arbor should prevent the bow spring from catching the front plate of the movement.

Check there is a gap between the minute wheel fitted to the cannon pinion and the hour-bridge.

The minute wheel must not rub the back of the hour-bridge.

Adjust the tension of the bow spring and the thickness of the hand-retaining washer.

If the movement runs with the hands replaced, check that the dial or dial pillars do not misalign with the movement in any way.

The dial must not obstruct the hands, hour pipe or seconds arbor.

hand and stopping the clock.

A very simple fault, easy to spot and rectify. However my friend had not spotted the hands catching, and was completely perplexed. He thought the fault must be more serious and lie elsewhere.

If only all faults were as simple.

One of the most common simple faults is that of a pendulum clock simply being out of beat.

A lot of owners of pendulum clocks do not realise that their clocks are not really portable and the pendulums should always be removed prior to moving the clock.

The pendulum bobs on some mantel clocks are relatively heavy, and moving the clock from one place to another can easily result in putting the clock out of beat and the clock failing to run after being moved. Gravity dictates that the pendulum will always hang vertically. If the case is subjected to a sudden movement this can disturb the relationship between the pendulum crutch and the pallets, especially if the crutch

and pallet arbor is a friction fit.

With the dial and hands removed check the depthing of the motionwork very carefully. The actual meshing of the motionwork should be on the loose side and must not bind in any way.

If a bow spring is fitted to tension the hands, the tension of the spring should retain the hands in place but also allow the hands to be adjusted quite easily.

If these checks do not reveal the problem the movement train and escapement will have to be inspected. Actual physical damage is usually easy to spot once the movement is removed from its case, but initially with the movement partly obscured it can be difficult to analyse the faults.

Before dismantling and attempting to diagnose the faults of any clock movement, you must have a good understanding of the operating principles of a basic clock movement and in particular the type of movement you are working on.

The movement should be removed from its case and the condition of the

Apply pressure to the great wheel of the going train.

With the pendulum removed the escape wheel should trip through the pallets.

If the train does not run the movement may be seized or some of the pivots bent or gear wheels/pinions damaged.

If the train runs, inspect the action and drop of the escapement

The drops on both pallets should be even and not excessive.

If the drops are excessive or uneven the pallets will need re-facing and adjusting.

If the pallets visibly 'lift' when engaging with the escape wheel teeth the pallet arbor holes require re-bushing.

Inspect the movement pivot holes for wear.

Any worn pivot holes will require the pivots to be re-polished and the pivot holes to be re-bushed.

movement assessed.

If the movement is clearly dirty and there are visible signs of dirty congealed oil, the movement will certainly require dismantling and cleaning.

With the power removed there should be audible/visible endshake to all the arbors when the movement is shaken.

In the case of a striking movement, check that the striking train is releasing and working correctly and is not causing the movement to stop.

Remove the motionwork and striking detent levers.

With the power removed and finger pressure applied to the great wheel, worn pivot holes become very evident. Any worn pivots can be seen to move excessively in their holes.

The pinions should be checked for 'pocketing' or wear. A combination of badly worn pinions and worn pivot holes can effect the depthing of the wheels and the efficient transfer of power from the motive force of the train to the

escapement.

If the pinions are very badly worn the meshing wheel may have to be moved on its arbor.

The escapement must function correctly; all power from the mainspring/weight must be used to drive the pallets and pendulum. As one tooth of the escape wheel is released by one pallet, the next tooth must be arrested by another.

If the clock is spring driven remove the mainspring and examine the spring.

Even if the spring is not damaged or fatigued there is always the possibility that it may have been replaced at some time by a spring of the wrong size or type.

Having thoroughly cleaned and re-assembled the clock, check the movement plates are pinned up tightly and that there is noticeable endshake between the shoulders of the arbors and the movement plates.

With the pallets removed ensure the train runs freely with no sudden

With the movement dismantled check for worn/damaged or bent wheel teeth.

Bent wheel teeth should be gently eased and straightened.

Check the concentricity of the wheels on their arbors.

A previous repairer may have moved a wheel and if not running concentrically the wheel could be 'butting' the teeth of the adjacent pinion.

Check the alignment of the movement plates and pillars when tightly pinned in place.

All clock mechanisms whether spring or weight driven suffer a certain amount of plate movement when fully wound. If the plates are distorted, not seated correctly, or not pinned-up tightly the distortion increases, leading to the wheels and arbors losing their freedom and ability to mesh correctly. A check should be made both with the wheel train in place and with the wheels removed.

stoppages.

The wheels should spin freely irrespective of the position of the plates.

The movement should be rotated and turned upside-down and the wheels should continue to spin regardless.

Any sudden stoppages should be investigated and the cause rectified before proceeding with the assembly of the rest of the movement, motionwork *etc.*

If the running of the train is giving problems, try the wheels individually then and in pairs.

Check very closely the depthing of any re-bushed holes.

A previously re-bushed hole may not have been re-bushed 100 per cent accurately, causing the wheel/pinion teeth to butt together.

The repair may have been acceptable to start with, but after a few years running and slight wear, the faulty bushing/depthing becomes apparent and is sufficient to stop the clock.

If the movement is built up in stages it should be possible to check the running of the movement at each stage and ensure that when fully assembled the clock

If the spring is contained in a barrel, remove the barrel cover and inspect the inside of the cover. Check the spring is not catching/marking the inside of the cover.

If the spring is too wide for the barrel it will scrape the inside of the cover and possibly unwind unevenly. Ensure the spring is the correct type and size for the movement.

Remove the spring and check the spring is not fatigued.

When removed from the barrel an efficient spring should expand quite considerably and retain its spring.

Examine the 'eyes' of the spring.

The eyes must not be torn and should positively locate on the barrel and arbor hooks.

works correctly.

When happy with the running of the going train, the motionwork can be fitted, and then, on a striking clock, the strike release levers fitted in place. Striking, chiming and calendar work puts a temporary but additional load on the motionwork and going train of the movement.

The effect of releasing the strike and changing the calendar should not have any effect on the movement or alter the rate of the clock. The clock should be kept on test for a couple of weeks during which time the rate of the clock should be noted and brought to time if necessary. With everything working correctly the movement can then be lubricated and put on final test. Experience has taught me not to oil the movement until I am completely happy with the running of the clock. If the clock is oiled and has to be dismanteld because of an unforeseen problem, the oil will smear the plates, which will then require re-cleaning.

Although correct lubrication is most important, a clock movement should be able run 'dry' for relatively short test purposes.

After oiling, the clock should still be left on test for another week or so and the timekeeping finely regulated.

Although the above list of likely faults and remedies is not exhaustive and there are many other possible causes for a clock stopping, a systematic and isolating approach to fault finding can help in both saving time and pinpointing the actual fault.

Readers will appreciate that I have restricted my list of faults and suggested remedies to a simple pendulum timepiece movement.

Balance wheel movements and other more complicated clocks may develop other faults and may require a different diagnosis.

APPENDIX 2
GLOSSARY

Arbor. An axle or shaft which carries a wheel or pinion.

Back cock. The metal bridge which holds the rear pivot of the pallet arbor, and from which the pendulum is suspended.

Beat. The oscillation or swing of the pendulum relative to the audible tick of the clock. When the ticks are even the clock is said to be 'in beat'.

Bob. The circular mass of the pendulum.

Broach. A five-sided cutting tool used to enlarge pivot holes prior to re-bushing.

Bush. A brass tube inserted into the plate to correct worn pivot holes.

Cannon pinion. Motionwork pinion located on and driven by the centre arbor, with a pipe that carries the minute hand.

Centre arbor. The arbor on which the centre wheel runs.

Centre wheel. The wheel in the going train that drives the cannon pinion, making one revolution clockwise every hour.

Click. A steel pawl used in conjunction with a ratchet wheel.

Clickspring. A spring which bears on the click allowing movement but returning the click into place.

Cock. A separate bracket or support usually held in place on the movement plate with a single screw.

Countersink. The enlarged upper part of a hole.

Countwheel. A specially cut wheel that determines the number of hours struck by countwheel striking movements.

Crutch. The arm which connects the pendulum to the pallet arbor.

Depthing. The name given to the optimum meshing of the wheels and pinions in a wheel train.

Dial. Face of clock.

Drop. On an escapement the interval between the release of one tooth on the escape wheel and the arrest of another.

Escapement. The mechanism that impulses the pendulum and regulates the rate at which the movement runs.

Escapewheel. The final wheel in the going train which impulses the pendulum.

Fly. A device used in striking movements to regulate the speed of the strike. An air brake.

Gathering pallet. A steel pin with a knife edge which rotates and gathers the teeth of the rack on a rack striking clock.

Going barrel. A brass barrel that contains the mainspring and drives the mechanism. The teeth are attached or cut into the wall or periphery of the barrel.

Going train. A series of connecting wheels and pinions calculated with ratios specifically to deliver power to the escapement and drive the motionwork of the clock.

Great wheel. The first wheel in the wheel train.

Hammer pin. The pin on the hammer arbor which lifts the hammer.

Hammer arbor. The arbor on a striking clock on to which the hammer is fitted.

Hand collet. A domed brass washer held in place on the centre arbor by a cross pin. The hand collet and pin retain the hands in place.

Hour wheel. The wheel which runs on the cannon pinion and on which the hour hand is fitted. The hour wheel gears with the minute wheel/pinion and makes one revolution clockwise every 12 hours.

Impulse. The determined force provided by the movement in order to keep the pendulum oscillating.

Intermediate wheel. In the going train the second wheel in the train to the going barrel or great wheel.

Leaf. Tooth of a pinion.

Lifting lever. Levers used and arranged to activate other components.

Locking arbor. An arbor in the striking train which operates on the strike stop wheel and locks the train.

Locking knife. On a countwheel clock the projection on the locking arbor which runs on the countwheel.

Mainspring. Coiled spring providing power to the movement.

Minute wheel/pinion. A combined wheel and pinion forming part of the motionwork. The minute wheel gears with the cannon pinion and the minute wheel pinion gears with the hour wheel in order to provide the 12:1 reduction required for the hour hand.

Motionwork. The wheels and pinions used to obtain the reduction in gearing for the hands of the clock. The motionwork also ensures both hands turn in the same direction. Motionwork is separate from the going train of the movement.

Movement. The clock mechanism

Pallets. A pair of specially shaped steel teeth that intercept with the teeth of the escape wheel at a regular interval.

Pendulum. The time regulating component of the clock.

Pillars. Metal bars holding the plates apart.

Pinion. A small wheel usually attached to an arbor consisting of less than 20 teeth, (typically 6 to 12)

Pin wheel. A wheel on striking clocks with pins at regularly spaced intervals. Used to operate the hammer arbor.

Pivot. The ends of the arbor which have been reduced in diameter and run in the clock plates.

Plates. Flat brass sheets drilled to accept wheel and pinion arbors.

Rack. The toothed component used on rack striking clocks to determine the number of hours struck.

Rack hook. The pawl that locates in the teeth of the rack preventing it from falling.

Rack tail. The projection on the rack which falls on the snail.

Ratchet wheel. A wheel with teeth cut at a steep angle. Used in conjunction with a steel click and return spring to ensure the wheel travels in one direction only.

Snail. A device found on a rack striking movement that via the rack controls the number of hours struck by the clock. Shaped like a snail shell ... hence the name.

Stop arm. Attached to the locking arbor on a striking movement. The stop arm engages with a pin on the strike stop wheel and arrests the train.

Strike stop wheel. The wheel in a striking train, which until released locks the striking train.

Striking train. The name given to the series of connecting wheels and pinions which operate the striking of the clock.

Suspension. The device usually used to suspend the pendulum from the movement.

Third wheel. The wheel in the going train between the centre wheel and escape wheel.

Timepiece. A clock movement that tells the time but does not strike or chime.

Warning. The time between the initial activation of the striking train and the actual striking of the clock.

Warning wheel. The wheel in a striking train which holds up the progress of the strike until released on the hour or half-hour by the lifting lever.

Wheel. Clock gear usually made from brass with more than 20 teeth.